Cat made a home
of sand.

It fell down.

4

Origins

A Home for Ted

Danny Waddell ◼ Jonatronix

OXFORD
UNIVERSITY PRESS

In this story

Cat

Ted

Cat made a home
of sticks.

It fell down.

Cat made a home
of card.

It fell down.

Cat made a home
of bricks.

It stayed up!

Find out more

Read about more homes in ...

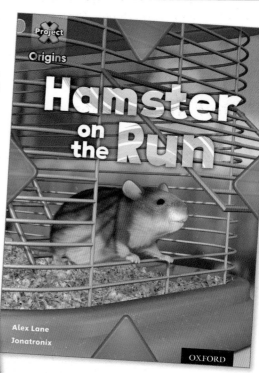

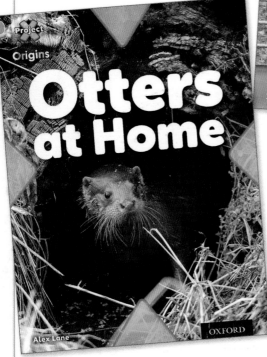